MW00630466

'Twas The Night Before Christmas

-A Christian Parody

Written by Emily Barreto Bares

Illustrated by Mohsin Khan

My sincere love and gratitude to:

Lee, my husband for always believing in me
Your love and encouragement meant the world to me.

Christopher and Crystal who cheered me on... you two are my heart.
My brothers and sisters... the bond we share is priceless.
My beautiful mother... gracias por tus oraciones mami querida.
My Crossroads family, my pastor and his wife,
and my life group ladies.

My dear friend Lisa who guided me every step of the way.
My friend Pastor Alex Garcia,
for allowing me the freedom to write this book.

To my granddaughter my sunshine and my joy
Zahara Marie
Love you my Princess, to the moon and back.

To my favorite teacher Coach Peterson
After all these years I never forgot your kind words
and positive encouragement. You would always say you enjoyed
reading my poems and I should follow my dreams as a writer.
You allowed me to believe in myself, and I thank you for that.

Copyright @ 2019 by Emily Barreto Bares

All rights reserved. No part of this publication may be reproduced, distributed, or transmitted in any form or by any means, including photocopying, recording or other electronic or mechanical methods, without the prior written permission of the publisher, except in the case of brief quotations embodied in critical review and certain other noncommercial uses permitted by copyright law.

Written and Published by Emily Barreto Bares

Printed in the USA

ISBN -978-0-578-42897-0

ISBN – 0-578-42897-0

This book is dedicated

to my angel in heaven

My Daddy

'Twas the night before Christmas

when all through the house

not a creature was stirring

not even a mouse.

The hay was selected

and put down with care

with hopes that baby Jesus

soon would be there.

An angel appeared

to Mary's surprise

the angel exclaimed,

"Mary arise!"

You were chosen a virgin

pure as can be…

to give birth to our Savior

for the world to see.

You will travel to Bethlehem,

Mary was told

in a manger you'll have him

where he will be born.

His name will be Jesus the angel then said,

just follow the star and you will be led.

So, Mary and Joseph

knew it was time

to travel Eastward

the star was the sign.

The journey was long

in the cold winter night

but they'd never get lost

as the star was so bright.

There were shepherds watching

their flock in the night

when suddenly they saw

a very bright light...

...and out of the sky

they heard a loud clatter

the shepherds jumped up

to see what's the matter!

An angel from God

appeared in a flash

and said to the shepherds,

"You must leave in a dash!"

The angel then told them, "Don't be afraid,

you've been chosen to bring the good news of the day.

The Messiah is coming to all you must say...

our Savior our Lord on this Christmas Day."

The shepherds got ready for a long winter's walk

while visions of their Savior were all they could talk.

Towards the East, walking they went

to find baby Jesus the one God sent.

A king will be born, the news spread through town

not just any newborn but one with a crown.

There were also Three Wise Men the story is told

who brought frankincense, myrrh, and treasures of gold.

To Jerusalem they travelled in search of their King,

to give baby Jesus the presents they bring.

So they walked, and they followed the star's radiant glow

that led them to the manger with gifts to bestow.

When what to their wondering eyes should appear

but sweet baby Jesus so precious ... so dear.

To the world he came

so pure and so humble

as they watched him lay

all in awe and in wonder.

"Our Savior is born..."

the shepherds exclaimed!

"The Messiah is here..."

The Wise Men proclaimed!

His eyes - how they twinkled, his dimples - how merry!

His cheeks were like roses, his nose like a cherry!

His small little mouth was perfect you see...

and ten little fingers as cute as can be.

His face was so tender, and he had a round belly

that shook when he giggled like a bowl full of jelly!

Oh, how precious to see such a sweet little boy,

and all of who saw him were filled with such joy.

The animals gathered

to see what's the matter

when hearing the laughter

and all of the chatter.

There were donkeys, camels,

roosters and sheep

all gathered around

to watch baby sleep.

He slept through the night

all cuddled up tight

sweet baby Jesus

what a beautiful sight.

Our King has arrived

for the world to see

his purpose on earth

is to save you and me.

Then the angels exclaimed

as they flew out of sight,

"Merry Christmas to all

and to all a good-night!"

Made in the USA
Lexington, KY
22 November 2019

57334389R00017